Stella

Stella

The Secret Birthday Message

MAGGIE

For Bill Martin

The Secret Birthday Message

Eric Carle

A TRUMPET CLUB SPECIAL EDITION

Published by The Trumpet Club
666 Fifth Avenue, New York, New York 10103

ISBN 0-440-84842-3

This edition published by arrangement with HarperCollins Publishers
Printed in the United States of America
January 1992
1 2 3 4 5 6 7 8 9 10
UPR

On the night before Tim's birthday he found a strange envelope under his pillow. He sat up straight in his bed and opened the letter. Inside was a Secret Message!

And this is what it said:

WHEN THE  COMES UP

LOOK FOR THE BIGGEST ★ .

BELOW IT YOU'LL SEE A ⬬ .

BEHIND THAT IS THE ▲ . GO IN .

LOOK UP TO FIND A ● . CRAWL THROUGH .

GO DOWN ▧

WALK STRAIGHT AHEAD TO A ▮ . OPEN IT .

YOU WILL SEE A ▬ CLIMB UP AND THROUGH .

THAT'S WHERE YOU'LL FIND YOUR BIRTHDAY GIFT!

HAPPY BIRTHDAY !

When the moon comes up

Look for the biggest star.

Below it you'll see a rock.

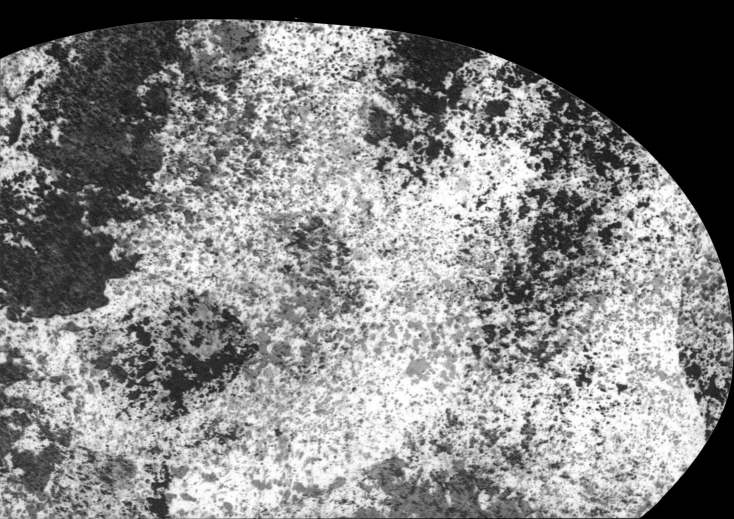

Behind that is the entrance to a cave.

Go in.

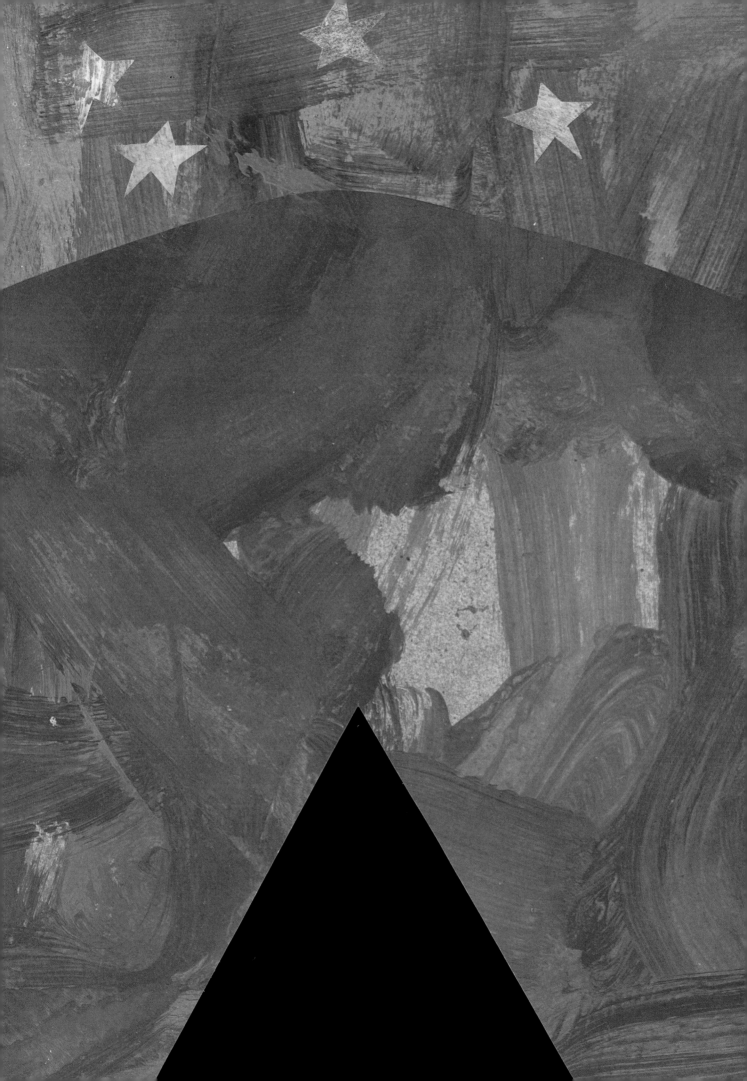

Look up to find a round opening. Crawl through.

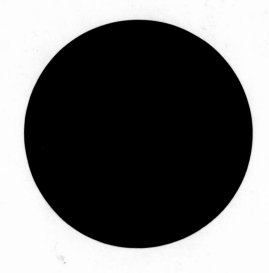

Go down the stairs.

Walk straight ahead to a door. Open it.

You will see an opening. Climb up and through.

That's where you'll find your birthday gift!

(Can you find your way back? See the next page!)

ERIC CARLE, internationally known author and illustrator, believes that children really enjoy learning, and his award-winning picture books reflect this conviction. Filled with color and humor, each of his strikingly designed books brings the child a happy lesson in counting, or reading, or provides a pleasant introduction to the days of the week, the seasons, or other basic concepts.

Born in the United States, Mr. Carle spent his early years in Germany, and studied at the Akademie der bildenden Künste in Stuttgart. His books have been published in Japan, England, and many countries in Europe, as well as in the United States.